Classic Stories
Mystery and Adventure

Level 3

Edited by Will Fowler
Series Editors: Andy Hopkins and Jocelyn Potter

Pearson Education Limited
Edinburgh Gate, Harlow,
Essex CM20 2JE, England
and Associated Companies throughout the world.

ISBN 0 582 465818

This edition first published 2001

Typeset by Pantek Arts Ltd, Maidstone, Kent
Set in 11/14pt Bembo
Printed in Spain by Mateu Cromo, S.A. Pinto (Madrid)

Published by Pearson Education Limited in association with
Penguin Books Ltd, both companies being subsidiaries of Pearson Plc

For a complete list of the titles available in the Penguin Readers series please write to your
local Pearson Education office or to: Marketing Department, Penguin Longman Publishing,
5 Bentinck Street, London, W1M 5RN.

Contents

Introduction

Suddenly, a crowd of enemy soldiers came running across the field, shouting wildly. The young soldier didn't have time to think. He threw his rifle into position and fired a first wild shot.

(Stephen Crane, *The Red Badge of Courage*)

One night, I woke up suddenly ... I thought I heard a sound ... Someone was walking about outside my room.

'Who's there?' I called. Nobody answered ... Then I heard a laugh. It was a terrible, cruel laugh!

(Charlotte Brontë, *Jane Eyre*)

People have always enjoyed telling stories and hearing them. Stories of adventure about brave men and women in danger have always been popular. And people have always liked mystery stories. They like them because they are exciting and a little frightening at the same time. But until about 1830 few people read them. In those days most people did not learn to read and write. Books were very expensive and readers did not usually spend money on fiction.

But after 1830 things changed very quickly. Almost all the stories in this book were written between 1830 and 1914. During that time, popular novels were published for the first time. As more people learned to read, businessmen produced magazines. These cost only a penny and came out every week. Many great novels in the nineteenth century were first printed in these magazines and later published as books. By 1870 everybody in Britain had to go to school and by 1900 almost everybody could read. The novelists wrote the kinds of story that interested ordinary readers.

The nineteenth century was a time when scientists were discovering new things every year. People were excited but also worried when they read the scientists' reports. What happens if an experiment goes wrong? Mary Shelley was the first to ask this question in a famous story, *Frankenstein*. Her scientist wants to create life but creates a monster. Many years later, Robert Louis Stevenson wrote a powerful story about a scientist who uses himself for his experiment. There is good and bad in everybody. But what happens if you can become two people, one good and one bad? This is the story of *Dr Jekyll and Mr Hyde*.

In those days, houses were dark at night because there was no electric light. It was easy to imagine ghosts there. And in other countries worse things probably existed. Bram Stoker imagined a vampire living in Romania. The vampire drank human blood. Readers today know his name, Dracula, because they have seen him in many films.

Ghost stories do not always need the dark to frighten us. Thomas Hood wrote a story about a man with two shadows. When one of the greatest novelists in English, Henry James, wrote a ghost story. The young narrator of *The Turn of the Screw*, a governess, sees the ghost during the day.

Sometimes the mystery in the house is about a person who lives in a room behind closed doors. Another young governess, Jane Eyre, wakes up in the night. She hears footsteps outside her door and someone with a cruel laugh. Who lives upstairs and frightens her? We read one of the great romantic novels of the nineteenth century to find out.

The first crime stories were written at that time. Until then there were no real police in many countries and crimes were often solved by private detectives. Sir Arthur Conan Doyle wrote about the most famous, Sherlock Holmes, but many years before that, the American writer, Edgar Allan Poe, wrote a story about a French detective, Dupin: *The Murders in the Rue Morgue*. In these stories the detective can solve the crime because he is more intelligent than the police. Writers like Agatha Christie copied the methods of Poe and Doyle.

We still enjoy reading stories about men who escape from prison. Of course the hero is not a criminal. He must be someone who has done nothing wrong. The French novelist, Alexandre Dumas, wrote the first famous escape story, *The Count of Monte Cristo*. Mark Twain's *The Adventures of Huckleberry Finn* is about a different kind of escape. Before the American Civil War there were still black slaves in the United States. Young Huckleberry Finn escapes from his bad father and helps a slave to escape.

The American Civil War produced one of the most powerful stories about war. In this story, *The Red Badge of Courage*, Stephen Crane imagined the feelings of a young soldier in his first battle. He wants to be a hero. But he is afraid that he will run away. Everybody imagined that Crane was an old soldier. The story is so real. But he was not even born when the war took place.

As the main European countries prepared for the First World War, two kinds of stories about spies became popular. The great Polish writer, Joseph Conrad, wrote *The Secret Agent*. This novel shows the world of spies as it really is. In this world, nobody is honest. The modern novelist, John Le Carré, writes stories like this. A more romantic spy story, with good spies and bad ones, is John Buchan's *The Thirty-nine Steps*.

Almost all these stories were written over a hundred years ago but they are still popular. There have been films of them all except the one by Thomas Hood; the same story was often made into a film many times. We have all heard the names of many of the characters – Frankenstein, Dracula, Sherlock Holmes. The writers of these stories showed the way to the best-selling writers of today, and their methods are the same. We love these exciting stories. We want to know what will happen next. Or we want to find the answer to the mystery.

1   *Frankenstein*   **Mary Shelley**

Mary Shelley (1797–1851) was the daughter of two writers, William Godwin and Mary Wollstonecraft. Her mother died when she was a baby. When she was seventeen, Mary fell in love with the poet, Shelley. He married her when his wife died two years later. In 1816 they were staying in Switzerland near another poet, Byron, and Byron said: 'Why don't we each write a horror story?' Mary's story, *Frankenstein*, is one of the most famous stories in British literature. She wrote other books after Shelley's death in an accident in 1822 but they are not popular today. *Frankenstein* is an interesting story with new ideas for its time because the monster is not bad. He only becomes bad when people are unkind to him.

Frankenstein lived happily as a child in Geneva in Switzerland. His parents also took a young girl, Elizabeth, into their home. Frankenstein was always interested in science. So when he was seventeen, his father sent him to the University of Ingoldstadt.

Frankenstein creates life

I arrived at Ingoldstadt and started studying. I was good at science and decided to give all my time to it. On my first day, my new teacher, Mr Waldman, told me to forget everything that I already knew.

'If you want to become a real scientist,' he said, 'you must learn all the sciences. But I want to teach you chemistry. That is an area of science that is growing. We are discovering new things all the time. So it is a very important subject.'

I listened carefully to Mr Waldman. He took me to his laboratory and showed me his experiments. I was very excited by everything that I saw. Mr Waldman gave me a list of new books to read.

At the end of the day I was tired but happy. I will always remember that day because it decided my future.

I became a good student. From the first day, chemistry was my favourite subject. Mr Waldman was an excellent teacher and I met the other scientists at the university. I worked on experiments in the laboratory all the time. Sometimes I stayed there all night until the stars disappeared from the sky. In the mornings, I was tired but happy. I went to my lessons, read a lot of books and understood more and more.

For two years I worked hard and did not visit Geneva. I wanted to discover where life came from. I wanted to experiment with science as much as possible. I wanted to create life. But first I had to understand death. I studied the human body. I also studied dead bodies. I was very interested in the change from life to death. I saw how a body changes. I learned how bodies are made.

And what was the result of all my experiments? I discovered the secret of life. I learned how to create life. I was very surprised and very happy. At first, I did not know what to do with my new powers. I could create life, but life needs to be inside a body. So I went to hospitals and looked at more dead bodies. I took parts of human bodies back to my laboratory. After a few months, I began to create a human form.

It was difficult work. I decided to make the person very large and tall. It was easier to work on a large body. I worked in secret in my laboratory at the top of the house. The summer months passed. The weather was beautiful, but I never went outside. I was too busy. I did not want to stop my work for anything. I forgot about my friends and my family. I did not write to them. I knew that my father and Elizabeth worried about me. I received letters, but I did not answer them. I thought only about my experiment.

Autumn came. My work was nearly finished, but my health was not good. I could not eat or sleep. I did not talk to anyone. Every night I felt ill and very nervous. I was afraid. But I could not stop.

One cold night in November, I saw the first result of my hard work. The body of the man in front of me had no life in it. It was one o'clock in the morning, and rain was falling outside. Nervously I used my tools to create life inside the body. Then I saw his yellow eyes open. He breathed and moved his arms and legs.

Success! The body was moving. After years of work, here was a human life! I looked at him. How can I describe my feelings? The man was terribly ugly. He had thick black hair and white teeth, but his skin was yellow and dry. His eyes were very pale. He was a monster.

After nearly two years of this experiment, I looked at the ugly monster and I was afraid. My dream disappeared. I ran out of the laboratory and went to my bedroom. I threw myself on the bed and tried to forget about the monster.

But when I fell asleep, I had wild dreams. I thought I saw Elizabeth. She was walking in Ingoldstadt. When I kissed her, her mouth became cold. It was like a kiss of death.

2   *The Count of Monte Cristo*
Alexandre Dumas

The French novelist, Alexandre Dumas (1802–1870), was the son of one of Napoleon's officers. His father died when he was a little boy. Alexandre grew up with a romantic idea of Napoleon and the history of France. When Napoleon lost the Battle of Waterloo (1815), kings returned to France. But Dumas's exciting stories helped the French people to remember their country's earlier success. The most famous are *The Three Musketeers* and *The Count of Monte Cristo*. There are many films of these stories. Dumas's son was also named Alexandre and he became a famous writer, too. His story of *Camille* was a great success as a film for the actress Greta Garbo.

Edmond Dantes, the hero of *The Count of Monte Cristo*, is a young sailor. His enemies say he wants to help Napoleon return to France. So he is put in prison. After many years there, he meets a man called Faria. Before his death, Faria tells him about a treasure on the island of Monte Cristo. But nobody has ever escaped from the terrible prison of the Chateau d'If in the port of Marseille.

Dantes escapes

On the bed Dantes saw a long bag of dirty cloth. The body of his friend Faria lay inside it. 'Alone! I am alone again,' Dantes thought. And then he stopped. He looked at the bag and a strange thought came to him. 'Only dead people leave this prison. I can take the place of the dead!'

There was no time to think about it. Dantes opened the bag with Faria's knife. He took the body from the bag and carried it to his own room. He laid the body on his bed and pulled the bedclothes over its head. Then he kissed the cold face and turned it to the wall.

'The guard will think that I am asleep,' Dantes said to himself.

He returned to Faria's room, took off his clothes and hid them. Then he got inside the bag, and lay exactly like the dead body. 'I have made my plan,' he thought. 'Will the men discover me when they carry the bag outside? Will they find a living man, not a dead body? If that happens, I will cut open the bag from top to bottom with the knife. Then I will escape. If they try to catch me, I will use the knife.

'Perhaps they will put me in the grave, and cover me with earth. It will be night. I only hope that the grave is not too deep.'

Another thought came to him. 'When the guard brings my evening meal at seven o'clock, will he notice Faria's body in my bed? But no, I am often in bed when the man comes. He just puts the food on the table and goes away again in silence. If he speaks to me this time, what will happen then? When he gets no answer, will he go to the bed?'

Dantes waited for the cries of the guard. But the hours passed, and the prison was quiet. Finally, Edmond heard footsteps outside. He must be brave now, braver than ever before. The footsteps stopped outside the door.

'There are two of them,' Dantes decided. He heard them put down some wood. 'They are going to carry the body on that,' he thought.

The door opened. Through the cloth of the bag, he saw two shadows come to the ends of his bed. Another man stood at the door.

'He was a thin old man, but he is heavy.' One man was lifting up his head. The other man lifted his feet.

'Have you tied it on?' the first speaker asked.

'Not yet – we don't want to carry unnecessary weight!' the other man replied. 'I can do that when we get there.'

'"Tied it on?" Tied *what* on?' thought Dantes.

The men put the body on the piece of wood. Then they moved up the steps.

Suddenly, Dantes felt the cold, fresh night air. The men walked about twenty metres, then stopped and put the body down. One of them went away. Dantes heard the sound of his shoes on the stone. 'Where am I?' he asked himself.

'Here it is. I have found it.'

Edmond heard the man put a heavy weight on to the ground next to him. Then he tied the weight round Dantes' feet.

'Is that tied carefully?' asked the other man.

'Yes. It won't come off,' was the answer.

The men lifted Dantes up again, and they began to walk. Now Dantes heard the sound of waves against the rocks.

'We are finally here,' said one of the men.

'Don't stop yet,' said the other man. 'You know very well that the last one fell on the rocks. Don't you remember that the prison governor was angry with us?'

They went five or six more steps, then they lifted Dantes by his head and by his feet.

'One!' said the men. 'Two! Three – and away!'

They threw Dantes into the air. He was falling, falling. A heavy weight pulled him quickly down. Finally, with a great noise, he fell into the cold water. When he hit the water, he gave a cry. Then the water closed over him.

'They have thrown me into the sea!' Dantes cried to himself. 'They tied a big stone to my feet. It is pulling me down to the bottom of the sea. This is the grave of the Chateau d'If – the sea!'

3 *Dracula*   Bram Stoker

Abraham ('Bram') Stoker (1847–1912) was an Irish writer. He wrote a number of stories but today he is known only for the story of the vampire, Count Dracula. Since *Dracula* there have been hundreds of vampire stories. But *Dracula* will always be the one that people think of. Dracula is an interesting character because at first he seems quiet and polite. But he is frightening at the same time.

Jonathan Harker is a young lawyer who works in London. Count Dracula has written to his company because he wants to buy a house in England. So they send Jonathan to Romania to help the count with his business. When he is near Dracula's castle, a woman gives him a cross. 'Wear it round your neck,' she says. 'Then you'll be safe.' Jonathan does not understand her yet.

First meeting with Count Dracula

Jonathan looked up through the trees. There was a large, black castle on top of a mountain.

'Castle Dracula, at last,' he thought.

Soon he was standing in front of a big, old wooden door.

Jonathan stood in the cold and waited, listening nervously to the wolves outside the castle walls. Then he heard a noise from the other side of the door. It opened. A tall man stood there, dressed in black.

'My house is your house,' he smiled. 'Come freely and go safely. Leave here a little of the happiness that you bring.'

'Count Dracula?' asked Jonathan.

'I am Dracula. I am glad, Mr Harker, to have you in my house. I will carry your bags – it is late, and my servants are asleep.'

Jonathan followed him up the stairs into a large, well-lit dining room. The room was warmed by a big wood fire. A hot meal was waiting for him on the table.

'Forgive me if I do not eat with you,' the count said, as Jonathan sat down. 'I have already eaten.'

After dinner Jonathan sat opposite the count by the fire.

'Your boss at the law company, Mr Hawkins, says many good things about you,' the count said. 'I am very pleased that you are here as my guest. I am not often able to practise my English.'

The count talked about his plans to move to England. Jonathan studied his face. It was an unusual face: very pale and mysterious with a long, well-shaped nose, cold, red eyes and a thin mouth filled with pointed, white teeth.

Silence fell at last, but Jonathan could still hear the frightening sound of wolves outside the castle. The count moved his face towards Jonathan's.

'My children are excited tonight,' he smiled. 'We have so few visitors.'

Jonathan smiled politely, but he felt sick at the smell of Dracula's breath. 'The smell of death,' he thought.

'Come,' Dracula said, standing up. 'It is getting light. You are tired after your long journey, and I have talked too much. Forgive me. I will show you to your room.'

◆

Jonathan slept late the next morning. He found breakfast ready for him in the dining room. There was no sign of the count, so Jonathan then decided to look around the castle. Many doors were locked, but one was open. Inside there was a large library. Jonathan was surprised that there were English books on the shelves and English newspapers on the desks. He spent the rest of the day there, reading happily.

In the late afternoon the count walked in.

'I am glad that you have found your way here,' he said. 'Since I decided to buy a house in England, I have tried to learn something about English life. I am sorry that I only know the language from books. I hope to talk to you, Mr Harker, and to learn it better. And now, our business.'

Dracula sat down opposite Jonathan and continued: 'Tell me about the house that your company has bought for me in England. There will be some papers that I must put my name to. Of course, I would like to know everything.'

'The house is called Carfax,' Jonathan began to explain. 'It's to the north of London. It has a lot of land. Most of the land is covered with trees, so it's quite dark. The house is large and old, with few windows. Next to it, there's an old, empty church. That also belongs to the house. I'm afraid that you will find Carfax a lonely house. Your only neighbour is a doctor who looks after a hospital for mad people.'

'I am glad that the house is old,' replied the count. 'I come from an old family and I do not like to live in a house without history. And the darkness does not worry me. I am an old man, and I often think about death. I do not fear darkness.'

He wrote his name on the papers and walked out of the room. Jonathan followed him into the dining room. Dinner was waiting, but again the count did not eat. 'I went out to eat today,' he told Jonathan. 'I am not hungry.'

That evening and the following ones passed the same way as the first. Then one day, about a week after he arrived, a strange thing happened. Jonathan was standing by the window. He was shaving in front of a little mirror from his travelling bag.

Suddenly he heard a quiet voice in his ear say: 'Good morning.' Jonathan jumped with fear and cut himself on the neck. The count was standing next to him. Jonathan looked in the mirror again, but he could only see himself.

'Why can't I see him in the mirror?' he thought.

He turned again, and saw a strange, hungry look in Dracula's eyes. The count was watching the small stream of blood coming out of the cut on Jonathan's neck.

Without thinking, Jonathan lifted his hand to the blood. As he did that, he touched the little silver cross around his neck. The count's face changed. His eyes shone red and he began to shake. Then, without a word, he picked up the mirror and threw it out of the window. There was a long silence, then Jonathan heard the crash of broken glass on the rocks far below. The count turned angrily.

'I will not have mirrors in my house,' he shouted. Then, seconds later, he said more softly: 'Try not to cut yourself. It is more dangerous in this country than you think.'

When the count left the room, Jonathan looked out of the window at his broken mirror. The ground was a long way down. For the first time he realized that he wanted to leave. He wanted to go home. 'But will he give me permission to leave?' he thought. 'Am I really his guest? Or am I, perhaps, his prisoner?'

Edgar Allan Poe (1809–1849) was an American writer with an unusual imagination. There was a film of his romantic horror story, *The Fall of the House of Usher*, in the 1960s, and seven more films followed. Poe also wrote one of the first crime stories, *The Murders in the Rue Morgue*. His detective, Dupin, is very intelligent. He notices details and so he is able to solve the crime. Detectives in the stories of later writers like Conan Doyle and Agatha Christie followed this method. Poe was always poor and his life was unhappy. His wife died in 1847, and two years later he was found in the street in Baltimore, very ill. He died soon after that.

The narrator of *The Murders in the Rue Morgue* is living in Paris. He has a French friend, Dupin. Dupin is a detective, and one evening the two men read about a strange murder.

The murders in the Rue Morgue

One evening, we were looking at the newspaper when we found a strange story. This is the story:

MYSTERIOUS MURDERS – At about three o'clock this morning, the people of the St. Roch neighborhood woke up when they heard terrible screams. The screams came from the fourth story of a house in the Rue* Morgue.

The house belongs to Madame* L'Espanaye and her daughter, Mademoiselle* Camille L'Espanaye. Eight or ten neighbors went into the house, with two policemen. The cries stopped, but the people could hear two loud voices at

---

Rue, Madame and *Mademoiselle*: French words for *street*, *Mrs* and *Miss*.

the top of the house. These voices stopped when they reached the second story. Everything became very quiet.

The police and neighbors began to search different rooms. The door to a large room on the fourth floor was locked, but they broke it down.

They found the room in wild disorder. The furniture was broken. A bloody razor lay on a chair, and there was a lot of gray, bloody hair on the floor near the fireplace. Many expensive things and two bags of gold also lay on the floor. The desk in the room was open, but there were things still in it. There was a small metal box under the bed. It was open, but there were only letters and unimportant papers inside.

Madame L'Espanaye was not there, but the dead body of her daughter was found in the chimney. The body was still warm. The face and neck were covered in blood.

The people searched the rest of the house, but they found nothing. Then they searched the small yard behind the building. Here they found the body of the old woman. Her neck was cut very badly. When someone tried to pick her up, her head fell off. Her body was also covered in blood.

Nobody has been able to solve this mystery yet. ...

... Dupin was very interested in the murders. "What do you think?" he asked me.

"I agree with the police and the newspaper," I said. "These murders are a mystery. I do not know how anyone can solve them."

"Do not judge these murders by the actions and reports of the police," said Dupin. "The Parisian police work hard, but they do not always see things clearly. They often look *too* closely. They make things too difficult. Sometimes, the true story is easily understood.

"So, why don't we try to solve these murders? First, we will go to the house and look at it with our own eyes. I know G——, the Chief of Police. He will let us in."

We went to the Rue Morgue. We found the house easily because many people were standing around it. They were looking up at the closed windows. Dupin looked at the street and the house very closely. I could see nothing important.

We knocked on the door and a policeman answered it.

"Your papers, please," he said.

We showed the policeman our papers, and he let us in.

We went upstairs to the room on the fourth floor. The bodies of the dead women were still there.

"Can you see anything unusual?" asked Dupin.

I saw nothing that was not described in the newspaper. Dupin looked closely at everything, even the bodies.

Then we went into the other rooms and into the yard. A policeman stayed with us all the time. We did not leave the house until dark. On our way home, Dupin stopped at a newspaper office.

Dupin said nothing about the murders until the next day. "Did you see anything strange in the house?" he asked me.

"No, nothing strange. Nothing more than we both read in the paper."

"The newspaper's opinions are not important. The police say that this mystery cannot be solved. It is too strange. But that is why we *can* solve it.

"First, the police do not know *why* the women were killed. Also, they cannot understand why two voices were heard upstairs. Nobody was up there, it seems, except the dead Mademoiselle L'Espanaye. Then there is the other information. There was no exit; the room was in great disorder; the daughter's body was up the chimney; the old lady was attacked in a terrible way.

"The police believe that the problem is difficult. It is difficult because it is strange. But an ordinary answer lies *in* the unusual facts—not outside of them. In a mystery like this, we do not ask, 'What has happened?' We ask, 'What has happened that has never happened before?' So I have solved the mystery easily. . . .

. . . "People heard voices, but they were not the voices of the women. . . . So someone murdered the ladies. The voices were the voices of the criminals. When you read the newspaper's descriptions of the voices, did you notice anything strange about them?"

"Everybody agreed that the rough voice belonged to a Frenchman," I said. "But they disagreed about the high voice."

"You have not noticed the important fact. Yes, people disagreed about the voices, but that is not strange. It *is* strange that five people, all from different countries, all heard the voice of a foreigner. And nobody could understand the language that was spoken.

"The voice was very unusual, but no words were heard clearly. No sounds *like* words were heard clearly. That is why I can solve this mystery. But I will not tell you my thoughts yet. First, let's remember the room on the fourth floor of the house.

"Which question shall we try to answer first? How did the criminals leave the room? . . . The door to the room was locked from the inside. The chimneys are too narrow for a person to climb. So the only possible exit was through the window. . . . The window, though, is on the fourth floor. So how did the criminals get down? A few feet from the window, there is a water pipe which goes to the ground. It does not seem possible that a man can reach the pipe from the window. The police thought so. But I was not thinking of a man. Think of the high voice that nobody could understand. Remember that no words were heard."

I began to understand. My friend continued.

"We know how the criminals got out. But nothing important was taken. The gold was left in the room. The ladies were not murdered for their money. There seems to be no reason for their murder. The police cannot accept this, but I can.

"Now, let's think about the dead bodies. A woman was killed and put up a chimney. No ordinary criminal does something like that. And the criminal was very, very strong. Five men were needed to take the body out of the chimney. Hair was pulled from the women's heads. The old lady's head was almost cut off.

"So, think: a bloody, terrible crime for no reason; the wild disorder of the room; the strange, high voice. What do you believe?"

"A madman did this!"

"Not a bad guess. But think of the voice. Even madmen come from somewhere. Even madmen have voices that you can understand. And a madman's hair is not like *this*." In Dupin's hand was a piece of strange hair. "I found this," he said, "in Madame L'Espanaye's tightly closed hand."

"Dupin!" I said, excited. "This is not the hair of a person!"

"No, it is not."

5 *Jane Eyre* **Charlotte Brontë**

Charlotte Brontë (1816–55) was the oldest of three sisters. They lived with their father in a little village in the north of England. The girls loved romantic stories and began to write them. Charlotte became a teacher. Then she went to Brussels to learn French. When she came home, she and her sisters decided to write for money. Her sister Emily wrote *Wuthering Heights* and Charlotte wrote *Jane Eyre*. The book is about a poor, plain girl who goes to work for a rich man. Jane falls in love with him. But she does not imagine he will ever love her. The novel made Charlotte famous but her life was very sad. Her sisters both died. A few years later she was married but she died, too, in childbirth.

Mr Rochester has employed Jane Eyre as a governess to teach Adèle, a little French girl. Jane lives with the housekeeper, Mrs Fairfax, and the servants until Mr Rochester comes home. She is happy there but one night something strange happens.

The woman in the attic

One night, I woke up suddenly. It was about two o'clock in the morning. I thought I heard a sound. Everything was very quiet. I listened carefully and the sound came again. Someone was walking about outside my room.

'Who's there?' I called. Nobody answered. I felt cold and frightened. The house was silent. I tried to sleep again.

Then I heard a laugh. It was a terrible, cruel laugh! I listened. Someone was walking away, going up the stairs to the attic. What was happening? I decided to go and find Mrs Fairfax. I put on some clothes and left my room. The house was quiet now, but suddenly I could smell smoke. Something was burning! I ran to find out.

The smoke was coming from Mr Rochester's room. I ran into the room and looked around. Mr Rochester was asleep in his bed, and the bed was on fire! 'What can I do?' I thought. Quickly, I looked around the room. Luckily, there was some water in one corner. As quickly as I could, I took the water and threw it all over the bed. Mr Rochester woke up.

'What's happening?' he shouted. 'Jane! Is it you? What are you doing?'

'Mr Rochester,' I said, 'your bed is on fire! You must get up now.'

He jumped out of bed. There was water everywhere and the fire was still smoking. 'Jane, you've saved me from the fire! How did you know about it? Why did you wake up?' Mr Rochester asked. I told him about the noise outside my door and the terrible laugh.

Mr Rochester looked serious and angry. 'I must go upstairs to the attic. Stay here and wait for me, please. Do not wake Mrs Fairfax.' He left the room and I waited for him.

At last, he came back. He was still looking very serious. 'You can go back to bed now, Jane. Everything is all right now.'

'Who lives in the attic?' I asked Mrs Fairfax the next day.

'Only Grace Poole,' she answered. 'She is one of the servants. She is a strange woman.'

I remembered Grace Poole. She was a strange, silent woman. She did not often speak to the other servants. So perhaps Grace Poole walked around the house late at night and laughed strangely outside the doors.

That evening, when Adèle finished her lessons, I went downstairs. Mrs Fairfax met me. 'Mr Rochester left the house early this morning,' she said. 'He is going to stay with his friends. I think he will stay with them for some weeks. I do not know when he will come back.'

For weeks, the house was very quiet again. Mr Rochester stayed with his friends and I continued my lessons with Adèle. I did not hear the strange and terrible laugh at night again. ...

... One evening, after Mr Rochester's return with his friends, a new visitor came to Thornfield Hall. He was a quiet young man with dark hair called Mr Mason. He came to see Mr Rochester on business. But Mr Rochester was not very pleased to see Mr Mason. When Mr Rochester heard the name 'Mr Mason, from the West Indies', he was surprised and his face turned white.

That night, Mr Rochester and Mr Mason talked for a long time. At last, very late at night, they went to bed. Soon, everyone in the house was asleep. Suddenly, I woke up. I heard a terrible scream from somewhere over my head. Then everything was very quiet again. I listened carefully, and then I heard a lot of noise from above my head. There seemed to be fighting in the room above. Then there was another scream.

'Help! Help!' someone shouted. There was more fighting. Then a voice called out, 'Rochester! Come quickly! Help me!'

A door opened, and I heard someone running up the stairs to the attic. I quickly put on some clothes and opened my door. Everybody in the house was awake now. The visitors were all standing outside their doors.

'What's happening? Is there a fire? What was that noise?' they asked.

Mr Rochester came down from the attic. 'Please don't worry,' he told his friends. 'Everything is all right.'

'But what's happening?' somebody asked.

'One of the servants had a bad dream and started to scream,' Mr Rochester said. 'But everything is all right now. Please go back to bed.'

Slowly, all Mr Rochester's visitors returned to their rooms. I too went back to my room, but I did not go back to bed. I sat and looked out of the window. The house was very quiet now. There were no sounds from the attic.

Then someone knocked on my door. I opened it. Mr Rochester stood outside. 'Jane, come with me, please,' he told me, 'but come quietly ... follow me.'

I followed Mr Rochester up to the attic. He unlocked the door of a room and we went inside.

'Wait here,' Mr Rochester told me. I stood next to the door. There was another door on the opposite side of the room. From behind this door I could hear a terrible sound. It was like an angry animal. Mr Rochester left me and went through this door. Once again, I heard that terrible, cruel laugh! Was Grace Poole behind the door? Mr Rochester spoke to someone inside the room, and then came out and locked the door again.

'Come here, Jane,' he told me quietly. I came into the room.

There was a large bed in the room. Mr Mason was lying on the bed. His face was white and his eyes were closed. There was a lot of blood on his shirt. He did not move.

'Is he dead?' I asked.

'No,' answered Mr Rochester. 'He isn't badly hurt but I must go and bring the doctor for him. Will you stay with him until I get back?'

The man on the bed moved, and tried to speak. Mr Rochester turned to him. 'Don't try to talk, Mason. Jane, do not speak to him, please. There must be no conversation between you.'

Mr Rochester hurried out of the room. I waited for him with the silent man on the bed. I was frightened. I knew that Grace Poole was in the next room. For a long time, I waited for Mr Rochester to return. 'When will he come back?' I asked myself.

At last morning came and Mr Rochester returned with the doctor. While the doctor was looking after Mr Mason, Mr Rochester spoke to me. 'Thank you for all your help, Jane. Mason is going to leave now. The doctor will take him away,' he told me.

We helped Mr Mason down the stairs and out of the house. It was still early, and the other people in the house were still asleep.

'Look after poor Mason,' said Mr Rochester to the doctor. 'Soon he will be able to go back home to the West Indies.'

Before he left, Mr Mason said something very strange. 'Look after her, Rochester,' he said. 'Promise to look after her.'

Mr Rochester looked sad. 'I promise. I will always look after her.'

I started to go back to the house. 'Don't go, Jane,' said Mr Rochester. 'Come into the garden. Talk to me.'

We went into the garden. 'What a night!' he said. 'Were you frightened, Jane?'

'Yes, I was frightened. Up there, in the next room ... there was someone ... that terrible laugh ... Mr Rochester, will Grace Poole go away now?'

I waited for him with the silent man on the bed.

'No,' he replied. 'But don't worry about Grace Poole. Try to forget about her. She isn't dangerous. It is Mason I am worrying about.'

I was surprised to hear this. 'Mr Mason? But he is frightened. He can't hurt you.'

Mr Rochester looked sad. 'I know Mason does not want to hurt me. But he could say something that will hurt me. I shall be happier when he goes back to the West Indies.'

6 *A Scandal in Bohemia* Sir Arthur Conan Doyle

Sir Arthur Conan Doyle (1859–1930) was a doctor, but as a young man he began writing stories about a detective, Sherlock Holmes. These soon made him famous and Holmes is still the best known detective in English. The narrator of the stories is Holmes's friend, Dr Watson, and this is the secret of Doyle's success. Watson asks all the questions that we want to ask. Holmes gives the answers and solves the crime. The answer often comes from unusual details. In this story, why does the young woman have to cut her hair and wear another woman's dress? Doyle was like Dr Watson, very polite to ladies. Holmes never marries and is not romantic. But in many stories, Holmes and Watson help a young lady who is in danger.

This story begins when a young lady visits Sherlock Holmes. She asks him to help her.

The copper beeches

One morning last spring I visited Sherlock Holmes. We were having some coffee when a visitor arrived. She was a pretty young woman. Her name was Violet Hunter.

'Please forgive me, Mr Holmes,' she said. 'I know that you are a busy man. But I would like your help.'

'Please sit down, Miss Hunter,' said Holmes. 'I shall be happy to help you. What can I do for you?' I could see that Holmes liked his visitor.

'I am a teacher,' she said. 'I lost my job two months ago. I looked for a new one but could not find one. I often visited an office in London which finds jobs for teachers. The business belongs to a woman called Miss Stoper. When I went in last week, a fat man was with her. He looked at me and turned to Miss Stoper.

'"This young woman is just right." he said. "If you come and teach my son, I'll pay you a hundred pounds a year."

'Well, Mr Holmes, I had no money and he was offering me a hundred pounds a year. It was a very good offer. He saw that I was surprised. Then he took some money from his pocket.

'"Here are fifty pounds," he said. "You probably need some clothes. You can buy them with this."

'He seemed a very kind person, Mr Holmes. I had no money. I could not even buy food. But why was he giving me so much money? I decided to ask a few questions.

'"Where do you live, sir?" I asked.

'"In a house called the Copper Beeches. It is in the country, five miles from Winchester."

'"And what will I have to do?"

'"I have a son who is six years old. You will look after him and teach him. My wife will sometimes ask you to do things. It won't be anything difficult. She will give you a dress and sometimes she will ask you to wear it. Will you do that?"

'"Of course," I agreed.

'"Sometimes she will ask you to sit near the window. Will you do that?"

'"Yes, I will."

'"And you will have to cut your hair short."

'As you can see, Mr Holmes,' said Violet Hunter, 'I have very long hair. I did not want to cut it short.

"'I am afraid not," I told him. "I don't like short hair."

"'Then I can't give you the job," he said. "I'm sorry." ...

... 'Well, Mr Holmes, I returned to my rooms. I had no food and no money. Did I do the wrong thing, I asked myself? These people seemed strange, but they were going to pay me well. And what use was my hair? I can't buy food with my hair. Perhaps I was making a terrible mistake. The next day I received this letter from the same man. I'll read it to you.

> The Copper Beeches,
> near Winchester.

Dear Miss Hunter,

Miss Stoper has given me your address. I have not yet found a teacher. Would you like the job? I can give you £120 a year and the work is not difficult. Sometimes my wife will ask you to wear a blue dress which belonged to my daughter, Alice. She lives in America now. She will also ask you to sit near the window sometimes. That isn't difficult, is it? But you will have to cut your hair short. I know that you would like to keep it. That is the reason that I am paying you so much. Please accept the job. I shall meet you at Winchester Station. Write and tell me the time of your train.

> Yours truly,
> Jephro Rucastle

'That is the letter, Mr Holmes. I would like to accept the job, but first I would like your help.'

'Well, Miss Hunter, you want the job, so you have to decide. I will say this. I would not like my sister to take the job. It is not a job for a young lady.'

'But they will pay me very well, Mr Holmes.'

'Yes, too well. Why are they paying you a hundred and twenty pounds a year? They can find someone for forty pounds a year. There has to be a good reason.'

'I would like to take the job,' said Miss Hunter.

'Then take it,' said Holmes. 'If you are ever in danger ...'

'Danger! Will it be dangerous?'

'I don't know,' said Holmes. 'But I will come at any time. Just send me a note if you need my help.'

'Thank you, Mr Holmes. I feel much happier now. I shall write to Mr Rucastle and I shall cut my hair tonight.' She said goodbye to us and left.

'What a nice young lady,' I said.

'Yes,' said Holmes, 'and we shall see her again very soon.'

Two weeks later, Holmes showed me a note from Winchester. It said: *Please come to the Swan Hotel in Winchester at midday tomorrow. It is very important. Violet Hunter. ...*

... The next day we arrived in Winchester and went to the Swan Hotel. Miss Hunter was waiting for us there, and we all sat down to eat.

'I am so happy to see you,' she said. 'You are both very kind. I don't know what to do. I need your help.'

'What is it?' asked Holmes.

'I have to be quick,' she said. 'I need to get back before three o'clock. They are not unkind – it's nothing like that. But I am quite frightened. When I arrived, Mr Rucastle met me. We drove to his house, the Copper Beeches. It's a big square house. In front of the house there is a field which runs as far as the Southampton road. The road is 260 feet from the house. There are some copper beech trees in front of the house and they gave the house its name.

'Mr Rucastle was very nice to me and I met his wife and child. Mrs Rucastle is a very quiet woman. She is Mr Rucastle's second wife. He also has a daughter from his first marriage. She is twenty and lives in America. She went to America because she did not like his second wife. That is what Mr Rucastle told me. Mr Rucastle is kind to his wife, but something is wrong. Mrs Rucastle is a sad woman and often cries.

'Two other people live in the house and work for the Rucastles. They are Mr and Mrs Toller. They are not very nice to me and I don't like them.

'For the first two days there was nothing unusual about my job. On the third day, Mrs Rucastle came down to breakfast and said something to her husband. He came to me.

'"Miss Hunter," he said. "My wife wants you to wear a blue dress. There is one on the bed in your room. Will you go and put it on?"

'I found a light blue dress on my bed. The cloth was good but it was not new. It belonged to another woman. It fitted me very well so I went downstairs. Mr and Mrs Rucastle were very pleased. We were in a room with a large window at the front of the house. There was a chair near the window and Mrs Rucastle asked me to sit in it. Then Mr Rucastle told me funny stories which made me laugh. But Mrs Rucastle did not laugh. She looked sad. Mr Rucastle told me funny stories for about an hour. Then suddenly he stopped and told me to change my dress.

'Two days later, the same thing. I wore the blue dress, sat near the window and Mr Rucastle told me funny stories. They made me laugh even more. Then he gave me a book and told me to read it to him. I read to him for ten minutes. But suddenly he ordered me to stop. I was very surprised because I was in the middle of a sentence.

'I always had to sit with my back to the window. Was something happening outside? I had an idea and the next day I hid a small mirror in my hand. Mr Rucastle was telling his funny stories and I was laughing. I put my hand to my eyes and looked in the mirror. A man was standing on the road, looking at the house. He was a small man with a beard and he was wearing a grey suit. Then Mrs Rucastle saw the mirror.

'"Jephro," she said to her husband, "there is a man on the road, looking at Miss Hunter."

*Was something happening outside? I had an idea and the next day I
hid a small mirror in my hand.*

'"Is he a friend of yours, Miss Hunter?" asked Mr Rucastle.

'"No," I said. "I know nobody here."

'"Then give him a sign to go away."

'I did that. Then Mrs Rucastle told me to leave the room. That was a week ago. That is the last time that I wore the blue dress. It is also the last time that I saw the man on the road.'

7   *Dr Jekyll and Mr Hyde*   Robert Louis Stevenson

Robert Louis Stevenson (1850–94) was born in Edinburgh. He gave up his studies at the university and travelled abroad for his health. In France he met Mrs Fanny Osbourne. A few years later he made a long journey to California to marry her. They returned to England and Stevenson began writing stories. His first novel, *Treasure Island* (1883), made him famous. Stevenson followed this with *Dr Jekyll and Mr Hyde* (1886) and with novels about Scottish history. In 1888, still suffering from poor health, Stevenson took his family to the South Seas. They lived on the island of Samoa until he died suddenly in 1894. Most of Stevenson's novels are full of exciting adventures but *Dr Jekyll and Mr Hyde* is more serious. It asks the question: 'Can the same man be good and bad?'

The story begins when two friends go for a walk. One tells the other about a bad man called Mr Hyde. The other is worried because Mr Hyde seems to have power over his friend, Dr Jekyll.

Who is Mr Hyde?

Other people could see no reason for Mr Utterson and Mr Enfield to be friends. Mr Enfield was quite different from Mr Utterson. He was younger, and enjoyed going to the theatre, to parties and good restaurants.

'Why are they friends?' people asked. 'What do they talk about when they are together?'

And the reply was: 'If you see them on their Sunday walks, they never say anything. They don't seem to enjoy themselves.'

But the two men thought that their Sunday walks were an important part of the week. They enjoyed being together, and they enjoyed the walks. But they were often silent walks.

On one of their walks the two men found themselves in a narrow street in a busy part of London. . . . Near one end of this street, there was a break in the line of shops. There was a narrow entrance to a courtyard, and next to it was the windowless end of a tall, dark, ugly house. A door in this wall was unpainted and needed repair. . . .

. . . Mr Enfield and the lawyer were on the other side of the street, but Mr Enfield pointed to it with his walking stick.

'Have you ever noticed that door before, John?' he asked.

'Yes. Ugly, isn't it?' replied Mr Utterson.

'Every time I pass it,' said Mr Enfield, 'I think about a day last winter. A very strange thing happened.'

. . . 'Oh?' said Mr Utterson. 'What was it?' . . .

. . . 'One dark morning, I was on my way home at about three o'clock. At first I walked a very long way without seeing anyone. Everybody was asleep. The street lights were lit, but the street was empty and silent.

'Suddenly I saw two people. One was a little man who was walking quickly towards the street corner. The other was a little girl. She was about eight or nine years old, I think. She was running as quickly as she could towards the same corner. Naturally, she ran into the little man.

'And then I saw something terrible. The girl fell down, and the man calmly *walked on her*. He stepped on her body! She cried out, of course, but he did not stop or turn round – he just walked away! He wasn't acting like a man – more like a mindless machine. Then the girl started screaming.

'I shouted and ran after the man. At last I caught him by the neck, and brought him back. Already there was a group of people round the crying child – her family, and some of her neighbours.

'"Get a doctor!" said somebody, and one of the neighbours hurried away.

'He was quite calm – the man who stepped on the child. He did not try to escape. But he looked at me once, and my blood ran cold. I hated him. . . .

. . . '"We'll tell all our friends about this!" we told the man. "Everyone in London will hear about it."

'And all the time, we were keeping the women away from him. They were wild and dangerous because they were so angry. I never saw so many hate-filled faces. And there was the man, in the middle. He was frightened, but he smiled an ugly smile and did not move.

'"If you want money," he said, "tell me. Nobody wants trouble with people like you."

'We told him to give a hundred pounds to the child and her family. At first he didn't want to agree to this, but the little crowd round him looked dangerous, and at last he said, "All right, I'll pay."

'Next, we had to get the money. And where do you think he took us? To that ugly place with the door! He pulled a key out of his pocket, unlocked the door and went in.

'We waited outside. After a time, he came out with ten pounds in money, and a cheque for the rest. The cheque was signed, and the signature surprised me. It was the name of a famous man! I can't tell you the name, but you probably know it well.

'"I don't like this," I said. "You walk through a door like that at four o'clock in the morning, and come out of it with another man's cheque for nearly a hundred pounds! It's very unusual."

'He smiled his ugly smile again and answered, "You don't need to worry. I'll stay with you until the banks open. And then I'll get the money with the cheque."

'The child's father, the man and I went to my house and waited there until the morning. After breakfast, we all went to the bank together, with the cheque. And the bank paid the money without question.' ...

... 'Oh, dear!' Mr Utterson said. 'That's a terrible story.'

'Yes, I agree,' said Mr Enfield. 'Nobody would like the unpleasant man who hurt the girl. But another man signed the cheque, and he is exactly the opposite. A really fine, honest man, and very famous for his good work.'

'What is the name of the man who walked over the child?' asked Mr Utterson.

'His name is Mr Hyde,' said Mr Enfield.

'And the man who signed the cheque? Does he live in that house?' asked Mr Utterson. 'Do you know?'

'Behind that door?' Mr Enfield said. 'No, he doesn't. His house is in a square, but I don't remember the name of the square. The place behind the door doesn't really seem like a house. There are three windows on the first floor over the courtyard. They are always shut, but they are clean. Somebody lives there. But the houses are all near together round the courtyard. You can't be sure how many there are. There doesn't seem to be another door. And nobody uses the door that I showed you. Except the man that I told you about.'

Mr Utterson walked in silence. It was clear that he was thinking. At last he said, 'Are you sure that he used a key?'

Mr Enfield was clearly surprised. 'Well ...' he began.

The lawyer continued, 'I'm sorry. It must seem a strange question, but there is a reason for it. I already know the name of the man who signed the cheque.'

◆

That evening, Mr Utterson ate his dinner without much interest. He was not really hungry. There was too much on his mind. After dinner he usually read a book and then went to bed.

But that night he took a light and went into his office. There he opened his safe and took out an envelope. On it were the words: *Dr Jekyll's Will*. He sat down and began to read the will with a worried look on his face.

The will was in Dr Jekyll's writing. Mr Utterson refused to help the doctor when he wrote it. The lawyer had to keep it for the doctor – it was his job – but he did not like the will.

The will was clear. *If Henry Jekyll dies, his house and all his money passes into the hands of his friend and helper, Edward Hyde. And if Dr Jekyll disappears for three months, the same Edward Hyde will own everything immediately.*

The lawyer disliked this will. He did not like it as a lawyer, and it made him angry as a person. He liked people to do things in an ordinary way.

'My dislike was very strong when Hyde was only a name,' he said to himself. 'Now I know some very unpleasant things about the man with that name, and it makes it worse. I thought that Jekyll was mad. Now I'm beginning to think he's afraid.'

8   *The Thirty-nine Steps*   John Buchan

John Buchan (1875–1940) was a Scottish writer and politician. When Buchan died, he was the King's representative in Canada. In the years before the First World War countries employed spies when they were preparing for war. Buchan's novel, *The Thirty-nine Steps*, was written soon after the war started. It was an immediate success. He followed it with a number of exciting adventure stories with the same hero, Richard Hannay. Alfred Hitchcock made a great film of *The Thirty-nine Steps* in 1935.

In 1914, just before the beginning of the First World War, Richard Hannay has returned to England from Africa. An American, Scudder, asks him for help. He has discovered a German plan to kill an important Greek politician. Hannay believes his story. He knows Scudder is in danger. So Scudder moves into his flat. But one evening when Hannay comes home ...

The milkman's escape

I walked into the next room and saw something in the corner. For a second I could not see what it was. Then I suddenly felt very cold and weak. I wanted to open my mouth and cry out. But I could not move or say anything. Scudder was lying on his back with a knife through his heart.

I sat down and felt very sick. I sat there for perhaps five minutes and then fear brought me to my feet again. Scudder's white face was too much for me. I covered the body with a tablecloth. I found a drink and sat down again. Scudder was dead and his body proved his story. His enemies killed him because he knew their plans.

'They'll kill me next,' I thought. 'They know that he lived on the top floor. They know that he was staying in my flat. And they'll guess that he told me their plans.'

What could I do? Well, I could go to the police and tell them the story. But there was the problem of Scudder's death. 'The police will think that I killed him,' I thought.

I thought about it for a long time and then I formed a plan. I did not know Scudder very well, but I liked him. I enjoyed an adventure too, and I wanted to continue his work. ...

... 'I'll go away for a few weeks,' I thought. 'Then I'll come back to London and go to the police.'

I went over to Scudder's body and took off the cloth. I searched his pockets for his book of notes, but the book was not there. He had no other papers.

Scudder was lying on his back with
a knife through his heart.

I opened my desk and took out a map of Britain. I thought that Scotland was the best place for my plan. I was born there and I spoke like a Scotsman. I spoke German very well too, and I thought about going to Germany. But perhaps Scotland was a better idea.

I chose Galloway because it was an empty part of the country. There were few big towns there, and it was not too far. I knew that there was a train to Scotland in the morning. It left London at ten minutes past seven. But how could I get out of the flat? Scudder's enemies were probably outside the building, so I had to leave secretly.

Then suddenly I had a great idea. Every morning at half past six the milkman brought my milk. He was a young man and we were the same size. He wore a white hat and coat. My idea was to borrow his clothes and the can of milk. Then I could get away from the building dressed as the milkman.

I went to bed and slept for a few hours. In the morning I counted my money and put fifty pounds in my pocket. While I was getting ready, I found Scudder's little black book and put it in my pocket. It was a good sign, I thought. Scudder hid it there, and his enemies did not find it.

It was twenty minutes to seven now, and the milkman was late. But suddenly I heard the noise of the milk can on the stairs, and I opened the door.

'Come in, please,' I said. 'I want to speak to you.'

He came into the flat, and I shut the door.

'Listen,' I said, 'you're a good man, and I want you to help me.' I took a pound out of my pocket and added, 'If you agree, I'll give you this.'

When he saw the pound, his eyes opened wide.

'What do you want me to do?' he asked.

'I want to borrow your clothes and your milk can for a few minutes,' I said.

He laughed. 'What do you want them for?' he asked.

'I can't explain now. Lend me the things, and I'll be back in ten minutes.' I put the pound into his hand.

'All right,' he said. 'I like a bit of fun too.'

I put on his clothes and we went out of the flat. I shut the door behind me.

'Don't follow me,' I said. 'I'll soon be back.'

I went down the stairs and into the street. I made a noise with the milk can and began to sing. A man was standing outside and he looked at me. He did not say anything. I looked at the house across the street and saw the face at the window again. I turned into another street and began to run. Then I took off the milkman's clothes and threw them, and the milk can, over a wall.

9 *The Man with Two Shadows and Other Ghost Stories* **Thomas Hood**

Thomas Hood (1835–74) was the son of a well-known writer of the same name. He wrote many books for children but also wrote stories for magazines. Readers liked stories about ghosts and mysteries that cannot be explained. This story, *The Man with Two Shadows*, is one of the best that was published at that time.

The narrator of the story says that his sister Lettie is always sad. She has never married because she lost her only real love, George Mason. Here the narrator explains what happened.

The picture on the wall

George Mason was my wife's cousin, a sailor. He and Lettie met at our wedding and fell in love immediately. George was a brave man and he loved the sea. I was not surprised when he decided to travel to the Arctic on the *Pioneer*. Lettie was afraid when he told her. But she could not stop him. I knew that she was worried. For the first time in her life, she began to look sad sometimes.

My younger brother Harry liked painting, so he decided to paint a picture of George. It was quite a good picture. I thought the face was too white. But Lettie was very pleased with it and she put it on the wall in our sitting-room.

Before the ship sailed, George met the ship's doctor, a Scotsman, Vincent Grieve. He brought him to dinner with us and I disliked him immediately. He was a tall, thin man with fair hair and cold, grey eyes. His face looked hard. I felt sure that he was not honest. He sat too close to Lettie and seemed more like her lover than George. At first George did not notice, but Lettie did and she was unhappy about it. The strangest thing was when he saw the picture of George on the wall. He sat down opposite it, but stood up again quickly. 'I'm sorry,' he said, 'but I cannot look at that picture.'

'Well, I know it's not very good ...' I began.

'It's not that it's either good or bad. I know nothing about painting,' he said. 'It's the eyes ... they seem to follow me everywhere.'

I thought that perhaps he just wanted to move closer to Lettie. But when I saw his face, he looked really quite frightened.

At the end of the evening, I quietly asked George about Vincent Grieve. 'Do you want to bring him to dinner again?' I said.

'No,' he answered. 'He's a good friend on the ship, but I don't like his way with ladies.'

We were all surprised when Vincent came again the next day. He brought a note for Lettie from George and after that he came almost every day. George was busier than him. He did not have so much time to see Lettie. On the last day before the ship sailed, Vincent said to Lettie, 'If anything happens to George, I will still love you. You can marry me.'

Lettie was very angry and told him to leave the house. She did not tell George about it because she wanted him to leave happily.

The time came for George and Lettie to say goodbye. When he left, Lettie cried for hours. I went in and put my arm around her. As I looked up, I noticed the picture of George on the wall. The face looked very, very white. I thought there was water on it. Perhaps it's just the light, I thought to myself. I tried to forget about it.

The *Pioneer* sailed. George sent two letters. Then a year passed before we heard anything. We once read about the ship in the newspaper, but that was all. Springtime came, and one beautiful warm evening we were all at home. The children were playing outside and Harry was watching them from the window. Suddenly the room felt very cold. Lettie looked up. 'How strange!' she said. 'Do you feel how cold it is?'

'Just like the weather in the Arctic,' I said. As I spoke, I looked at the picture on the wall. I suddenly felt terribly afraid. His face looked like a dead man's, with no eyes. Without thinking, I said, 'Poor George!'

'What do you mean?' asked Lettie, looking frightened. 'Have you heard something about George?'

'No, no,' I said quickly. 'I was just thinking about the cold weather where he is.'

10 *The Return of Sherlock Holmes*
Sir Arthur Conan Doyle

Sir Arthur Conan Doyle (1859–1930) was a doctor, but as a young man he began writing stories about the detective, Sherlock Holmes. They were an immediate success but Doyle became bored with Holmes and wrote a story about his death. Readers were very unhappy; they wanted more stories about their hero. So Doyle had to bring him back to life in this book. Doyle took the character of Holmes from Professor Bell, one of his teachers at university. Bell used little details to guess people's jobs and activities. Holmes uses the same method here when he looks at a pair of glasses.

The police in the early Sherlock Holmes stories are stupid. They are angry because he solves crimes for them. But in this story a young detective, Hopkins, asks Holmes to help him.

The golden glasses

'Yoxley Old Place is a large house in the country, near a small village,' said the detective. 'About ten years ago an old man, Professor Coram, came to live there. He was ill, and walked with a stick. After a few months, his neighbours became friendly with him, but they didn't often visit his house. They say he's very clever. He spends most of his time working with his books. He has a gardener, Mortimer, and two servants. The cook is Mrs Marker and the other servant is Susan Tarleton. They're good servants, and they've been with him for a long time.

'The professor is writing a book. About a year ago, he decided to employ a secretary. A man came, but he wasn't very good and he didn't stay very long. A second man came. He was called Smith. He became a good friend and helper to the professor. They worked together every day, and the book's nearly finished. But now the young man is dead. And I think someone killed him.

'As I said before, very few people visit the house. The people in the house don't go out very often either. Old Mortimer lives in a little house in the garden.

'Yoxley Old Place is near the London road. A visitor can easily go through the garden gate to the house, get in and escape quite quickly.

'I spoke to Susan Tarleton, the servant girl. She was working in one of the bedrooms between eleven and twelve o'clock this morning. Professor Coram was still in bed; he often gets up late. Smith was in his bedroom, reading a book. After a few minutes she heard him go down to the professor's study. Suddenly she heard a very loud cry. She ran down to the room. She found Mr Smith lying on the floor. He was nearly dead. There was blood on his neck, and a lot more on the floor.

'Mr Smith said a few words in a weak voice before he died. Susan Tarleton thinks he said, "The professor – it was she."

'I spoke to the cook next. She arrived in the room after Mr Smith died. The two women quickly went to the professor's bedroom. He was still in bed. He, too, heard the loud cry, but he can't get out of bed without help. Mortimer has to help him get up at twelve o'clock every day.

'I spoke to the professor. He can't think of any reason why Mr Smith was killed.

'Mortimer got the police, and they sent for me. When I arrived, I told everyone not to walk on the garden path. Nothing in the house was moved either.

'I think that someone very clever came to the house this morning. There were no footprints on the garden path. But I saw signs that someone walked along the grass near the path. That person didn't want anyone to know about his or her visit to the house.

'I went to the study and looked at Mr Smith's body. There was a small knife on the floor. I think he was killed with that. It's the professor's, and he always kept it on the table in that room. And we found these.'

He gave Holmes a pair of glasses. Holmes took them and looked at them very carefully. After a few minutes, he took a piece of paper and wrote something on it. Then he gave it to Stanley Hopkins. Hopkins read the note.

'Look for a woman who has plenty of money. She wears good clothes, has a thick nose, and her eyes are close together. She looks closely at things. She has probably visited an optician more than twice during the last two months. Her glasses are unusually strong, and quite expensive. There are not many good opticians in London, so you can find her name easily.'

The detective was surprised when he read this. I was, too. Holmes looked at our faces and laughed.

'Glasses can tell us many things about the people who wear them,' he said. 'These glasses belong to a woman – they're very pretty. Mr Smith said "it was she" before he died. That, too, tells me that a woman was there. She has money and likes good things. Why? Because the glasses are made of gold. And they're made for a thick nose, and eyes that are close together.'

'But how did you know that she looks closely at things? And about her visits to the optician?' I asked.

Holmes replied, 'These glasses are very strong, so the woman has very weak eyes. People with weak eyes always look closely at things to see them better. And the optician? It's clear that the glasses were mended twice, at different times. Can you see here? The gold is very new and yellow. Here it's a little older.'

Hopkins said, 'You're always so clever, Mr Holmes. You know more about this case than I do now. And you've never been to Yoxley Old Place! Will you and Dr Watson come there with me tomorrow?'

11   *The Red Badge of Courage*   Stephen Crane

Stephen Crane (1871–1900) wrote *The Red Badge of Courage* when he was only twenty-four. After the Battle of Waterloo (1815), Britain did not fight in a great war for almost a hundred years so very few war stories were written there. But there was a terrible Civil War in the United States (1861–5). In this book Crane imagined how a young soldier feels in his first battle. It is very real. Everybody thought the book was written by a soldier. The book made Crane famous and he went to Europe. He became the friend of the great American writer, Henry James, but died a few years later.

In this story, Henry Fleming has joined the army. He dreams of fighting for his country and being a hero. He is impatient to take part in a battle. But when the battle begins, he asks himself: "Will I be brave, or will I run away?" The red badge of courage in the title of the book is a wound. A wound is a sign that a soldier has fought bravely in a battle.

Into battle

The regiment marched into the forest. Henry began to worry again. "Will I be brave, or will I run away?" he asked himself. He thought about dying, and a new idea came to him. "If I die, I'll be able to rest." He began to feel less afraid.

Just then, he heard the sound of cannon fire. He saw a group of soldiers running and firing. He heard the sound of their rifles. The regiment on his right was standing and firing all together. He watched them through a cloud of smoke. The noise grew louder.

Suddenly, he felt a heavy hand on his shoulder. It was the loud soldier. "It's my first and last battle," he said sadly. "I'm sure that I'm going to die." He had tears in his eyes and his hands were shaking. He gave the young soldier a small package in a yellow envelope. "There are some letters inside. I want you to give them to my family."

"What do you mean?" cried Henry. But there was no reply. The other soldier walked away.

Henry's regiment stopped outside a wood. Through the trees, they could see some open fields and a thick cloud of smoke. In the smoke they could see a line of men running toward them. A team of horses ran with the men, pulling cannon on wheels.

A shell screamed over their heads and landed in the woods near them. A cloud of brown earth flew up into the air and showered down on them. Bullets hit the trees where they were hiding. The soldiers stayed very close to the ground.

They heard a loud cry of pain. A young officer was shot in the hand. Another officer covered his wound with a clean piece of cloth.

Far away, there was smoke and fire all around. Men in blue came out of the smoke, running like wild horses. More and more men ran toward the regiment, shouting. Their voices mixed with the sound of the bullets and the shells. As they came closer, the older regiments began to laugh at them. "What's the matter? What are you afraid of?" they called. "Are you trying to hide?"

Officers on horseback were hitting them and kicking them. "Stop! Go back!" they cried. The running men didn't see or hear them.

Henry saw the fear on their faces. He wanted to run, but he couldn't. His legs refused to move. "What are they running from?" he asked himself. "I want to see it. But when I see it, maybe I'll run, too!"

The young soldier only had to wait for a few minutes.

"They're coming!" cried a voice.

The men checked their rifles. Henry had a terrible thought: "Is there a bullet in my rifle?"

A general stopped his horse near another officer on horseback. "You have to stop them!" he shouted angrily.

"Yes, General," the officer replied nervously. "We'll try!"

The man next to the young soldier was talking to himself: "Oh, no, we're in trouble now!"

A young officer stood at the back of the regiment. "Don't fire, boys! Wait until I tell you! Wait until they come close!"

Suddenly, a crowd of enemy soldiers came running across the field, shouting wildly. The young soldier didn't have time to think. He threw his rifle into position and fired a first wild shot. He immediately began to work like a machine. He put in another bullet. He fired his rifle, again and again. He suddenly forgot about himself. He was part of the regiment and part of the army. His country was in danger, and he had to protect it.

12   *The Turn of the Screw*   Henry James

Henry James (1843–1916), the great American novelist, was born in New York but lived for most of his life in Europe. He studied British and French writers before he began his work. Most of his novels compare European and American society but he wrote one famous ghost story, *The Turn of the Screw*. As we read the story, we ask these questions: Are the ghosts real or is the young woman imagining them? If they are real, are the children in danger? If they are in danger, can she save them? The title tells us what sort of story this is. The writer is turning the screw on the reader. We feel the fear and danger that the young woman feels.

The narrator of the story is a governess. A man has employed her to teach two young children. She is alone in the house with the housekeeper, Mrs Grose, and the servants. One evening she thinks she sees a strange man on the roof of the house …

The face at the window

One evening in June, I walked about three miles through the park. When I came back to the house, I looked up and saw a face. Was it my employer's face? No, it was not. I realized that very quickly. A man stood on the roof of the tower. There were two towers, one at each end of the roof. Each tower had a room inside and you could climb out on to the roof from them. The little girl, Flora, took me there on my first day. I did not know this man. I saw him very clearly, and he was watching me. He stood and stared at me for a minute, then turned away.

I was frightened. Was there a secret in this old house? I wanted to ask Mrs Grose. But when I came back into the house, everything seemed quite ordinary again. I did not say anything to her, but for many days I thought about it. Finally, I decided: 'It was a stranger who found a way into the house. But he's gone now, so I can forget him. I won't worry about it.'

But one Sunday, in the early evening, Mrs Grose and I decided to go to church together. My bag was in the dining-room, and I went in there to get it. Suddenly, I looked up and saw a face at the window. It was staring at me through the glass. It was the man who I saw on the roof. I stared at him; he stared at me. I did not know him. But I felt, strangely, that I knew him very well. Then he looked round the room.

'He's looking for someone, but not for me!' I realized.

Then I felt brave. I ran outside and looked for him. But he was not there. The garden was empty. I went back to the window, put my face against the glass, and stared in. Mrs Grose walked into the dining-room, and saw me. She turned white. Then she came outside to meet me.

'Why is *she* frightened?' I asked myself.

'What's the matter?' she asked me. 'Your face is white. You look terrible.'

'*My* face?' I said. 'I was frightened. You saw my face at the window. But when I was in the dining-room, I saw a man's face in the same place.'

'Who is he? Where has he gone?'

'I have no idea.'

'Have you seen him before?'

'Yes – once. He was standing on the roof of the tower.'

'And you didn't tell me? What was he doing there?'

'He looked at me – that's all. He was a stranger, a terrible man.'

Suddenly, I looked up and saw a face at the window.

Mrs Grose looked out over the gardens once more, then said, 'Well, it's time for church now.'

'No, I can't go to church. Not now. I can't leave the children. It's not safe.'

'It isn't safe?' she asked.

'He's dangerous!' I replied.

She realized something then. I could see it in her face.

'What did he look like?' she asked.

'He is like nobody!'

'What do you mean?'

'He has no hat!' She looked worried, so I continued quickly, 'He has red hair, and a long face, with strange eyes.'

Mrs Grose's mouth was open, and she stared at me. 'Is he handsome? How is he dressed?'

'Oh, yes, he's handsome. And he's wearing another person's clothes.'

'The master's!' she said.

'You know this man?'

She did not reply for a second, then she answered, 'Quint. Peter Quint. He was the master's servant. He took some of his clothes – but never his hat. When the master left, Quint looked after everything in the house. He was only a servant, but he gave the orders.'

'Then where did he go?'

'Go?' she said. 'Oh no, he died.'

'Died?' I almost screamed.

'Yes,' she said. 'Peter Quint is dead.'

13   *The Adventures of Huckleberry Finn*   Mark Twain

Samuel Langhorne Clemens ("Mark Twain") (1835–1910) grew up in a small town in Missouri before the American Civil War.

Missouri was one of the states where people kept black slaves. Before he began writing, Clemens worked on boats in the Mississippi river. After that, he went to Nevada to look for gold. Most of his books are funny and many are really for children. Huckleberry Finn is a character in one of them, *The Adventures of Tom Sawyer*. But Clemens wrote two great novels for adults, *The Adventures of Huckleberry Finn* and *Puddn'head Wilson*. One of the questions these novels ask is: Are we really better than other people because their skin is a different colour?

Huckleberry Finn lives with the Widow Douglas but he runs away. His father has come back to town and Huck is afraid of him. He goes to an island in the river and meets Jim, the Widow Douglas's slave. Jim has run away, too. He thinks the Widow wants to sell him. Huck and Jim go down the Mississippi river and find a raft. They want to sail to the town of Cairo. At Cairo the river passes another state, Ohio. There are no slaves there and Jim will be free. But if they pass Cairo, the boat will go south to other slave states.

Lost in the fog

We were very close to Cairo now, and Jim was very excited. He said, "When we get to Cairo, I'll be a free man! They don't have slaves there."

Every time we passed a light, Jim jumped up. He said: "Look! It's Cairo! I'm a free man!"

So I told Jim: "In the morning I'll ask somebody what town this is."

But that same night, two men came over in a boat. They had guns too. One of the men said, "Who's over there?"

I said, "It's me and my raft."

"Are there any men on that raft?" he asked.

"Only one," I said.

"We're looking for five runaway slaves. Is the man on your raft white or black?" he asked.

"He's white," I answered.

"I think I'll check," said the man.

"Please do," I said. "It's Pap that's with me. Maybe you can help take him into town. Pap is sick — and so is Mom and my sister, Mary Ann."

They agreed to help and started coming over to us. Then I said, "It's good of you to help. I've talked to a lot of people, but nobody wanted to help."

"That wasn't very nice of them," said the man. "What's the problem with your pap?"

"It's the—it's the—it's nothing, really."

Then they stopped. "That's a lie, boy," the man said. "What *is* the problem with your pap? I want a true answer this time."

"I'll tell you, sir," I said. "But first come and help us get to town."

"Stop the boat, John," the man shouted. "You keep away, boy. If your pap is so sick, I don't want to come near him. Go about twenty miles down the river and you'll find a town. They can help you there." Then he said, "Do you have any money, boy?"

"No, sir," I said.

"Here's twenty dollars—that will pay for the doctor."

He put the money on a piece of wood and pushed it over to me.

I said, "Thank you very much, sir. I'll remember what you told me. Goodbye."

They both said, "Good luck."

When they were gone, I looked for Jim. He wasn't in the tent, so I shouted for him: "Jim, where are you?"

"Here I am," answered Jim. He was in the river. Only his head was above the water.

He got back on the raft and said, "I heard the men coming and

I jumped into the river. I didn't want them to find me. I was going to swim away. But you tricked them, Huck. That was a good story. You saved my life. Nobody has ever helped me like that. You're the best friend that I have."

We talked about the money.

Jim said, "I'm a free man, so I'll buy a ticket on a steamboat."

The next morning, we hid the raft and I went into town. I asked a man: "Is this town Cairo?"

"No," the man said, "You've gone past Cairo."

So I went back to the raft and told Jim. He wasn't a free man now. I felt really bad about going past it. But Jim said, "Huck, it's OK, I'll be free some day. Don't you worry."

◆

We slept all day, and the next night the fog came again. Jim and I were talking on the raft. We couldn't see anything and then we heard a steamboat. She was coming up the river but we couldn't see her.

The sound got louder. Then we saw her. She was coming straight for us! She was coming fast, too. Jim jumped off the raft and I jumped off too. I swam straight down because I didn't want the boat to hit me. I was under water for a minute and a half. When I came up, I called for Jim. He didn't answer. I looked for the raft, but it was in pieces. The steamboat destroyed it.

I couldn't do anything about that, so I swam about two miles to the side of the river. When I climbed out, I looked for Jim again. I shouted for him, but he didn't answer. This time I was sure that he was dead.

14   *The Secret Agent*   Joseph Conrad

Count Teodor Korzeniowski ('Joseph Conrad')(1857–1924) was born in Poland when part of it belonged to Russia. His father and mother wanted Poland to be free but they both died in a Russian prison. Conrad left home when he was seventeen. He became a sailor. After a few years, he was a captain on British ships. In 1894 he left the sea and started writing in English, his fourth language! His first books are about the sea but some of the later ones are political. *The Secret Agent* is the first modern novel about spies. But the book is really about the way that politics changes the lives of ordinary people.

In this story, Mr Verloc, a shopkeeper, lives with his pretty young wife, Winnie, and her brother, Stevie. Winnie married him because she needed a home for Stevie. He has the mind of a little child. People think that Verloc is the friend of anarchists. Anarchists are people who do not believe in any government. But Verloc is really a secret agent who works for the Russian Embassy. Now the Russians want Mr Verloc to do something for the money that they give him.

A dangerous plan

'Why did you ask me to come here to the Embassy at eleven in the morning?' asked Mr Verloc, a little angry. He was better with words than with actions. He was unhappy that this young man wanted him to do something. 'It's dangerous for me to come here in the morning. If someone sees me, I'll stop being useful to you.'

'That's your problem,' said Mr Vladimir. 'When you stop being useful, we stop paying you.'

Mr Verloc's legs felt weak and he suddenly wanted to sit down.

'We want action,' Mr Vladimir continued. 'But I don't mean that people have to die. We just want to frighten people. Buildings are enough. But which buildings? That's the question. What do you think, Mr Verloc?'

Mr Verloc didn't know. He said nothing. He was frightened.

'I'll tell you,' Mr Vladimir said. 'Today people love science.

They thank science for their comfortable lives. So if we want to frighten them, we must attack a science building. The newspapers won't be able to use all their old, tired words to talk about *that*. Usually, when a bomb attack happens, on a king, perhaps, or a theatre, people just say, "Oh, some poor people did that." And then they forget about it. But what about a bomb attack which people can't explain? *Then* they'll wake up. And it must be a famous building. I'll tell you the building that I'm thinking about. Can you guess?'

Mr Verloc just stood there, saying nothing. Mr Vladimir rested his arms on his desk, looked up at Mr Verloc and continued: 'The Greenwich Observatory!* You see? Everyone in the world, rich and poor, has heard of the Greenwich Observatory. It's perfect!'

Mr Vladimir looked very pleased with himself. 'It won't be easy,' was all that Mr Verloc could say.

'What's the problem?' asked Mr Vladimir. 'You have a large group of anarchists, haven't you?' . . .

. . . 'It will cost money,' Mr Verloc said.

'Don't worry,' said Mr Vladimir. 'We'll still pay you every month – but first we must see some action. And if nothing happens soon, we'll stop paying you anything. What's your job – I mean, when you're not working for us?'

'I keep a shop,' answered Mr Verloc.

'A shop! What sort of shop?'

'Oh, newspapers and things. My wife . . .'

'Your wife? You're married? And you call yourself an anarchist!'

'Well, my wife isn't an anarchist. And it's none of your business.'

'Oh, yes, it is,' said Mr Vladimir. 'I'm not sure now that you're the man for the job.' He was silent for a short time, thinking.

*The Greenwich Observatory: a famous building where scientists study the stars.

Then he said, 'You can go now. You can have a month. There must be a bomb by then. Is that clear? If nothing happens, you'll stop working for us.'

Extract Wordlist

anarchist	someone who is against all forms of government
army	all the soldiers who fight for a government
attic	a room at the top of a house
badge	something that you wear as a sign
battle	a fight between two armies
bomb	something that can destroy people or houses
breath	the air that comes out of your body
breathe	to take air into your body and let it out again
bullet	a small piece of metal fired from a gun
cannon	a very large gun, sometimes on wheels
case	something that a detective tries to solve
castle	a big building that protected people from attack
chemistry	the scientific study of what things are made of
chimney	a pipe that takes smoke out through the roof
copper beech	a kind of tree
count	a title of an important man in Europe (but not in Britain)
courage	the feeling that makes a person brave
courtyard	an open space with walls or buildings round it
create	to make something new
cruel	wanting to hurt other people or make them sad
embassy	the office of a foreign country in your country
experiment	a scientific test
fog	thick air that is difficult to see through
footprints	signs of people's feet or shoes on the ground
governor	a person with **power** over other people in a place
grave	a place where people are put after their death
human	of a person or people
laboratory	a place where scientists do tests

lawyer	a person who explains the law
mad	ill, not able to act like a sensible person
march	to walk like a soldier
master	the boss (when a servant is speaking about him)
monster	a large, ugly, frightening animal in a story
optician	a person who tests people's eyes for new glasses
power	if you have it, other people follow your orders
professor	one of the more important teachers at a university
raft	a flat boat made of pieces of wood
razor	a tool used for shaving
regiment	a large group of soldiers
rifle	a long gun fired from your shoulder
safe	a strong box where you keep money or papers
scandal	terrible actions that other people talk about
screw	a piece of metal – you turn it to join pieces of wood or metal
secret agent	someone who tries to get information about another country for their government
servant	someone who lives as an employee in another person's house
shell	a big bullet or bomb fired from a gun
slave	someone who belongs to another person
stare	to look at someone for a long time
steamboat	a big ship on the river
tower	a tall part of a building
widow	a woman who has not married again after her husband's death
will	a paper that other people read after your death – it says who must get your money and other things.
wolf	a wild animal like a large dog
wound	a bad cut made by a knife or bullet

ACTIVITIES

Stories 1–4

Before you read

1 Do some stories frighten you? What are they about? Why are stories like this popular?

2 Find these words in your dictionary. They are all in this book.

character   hero   narrator   novel   poet   vampire

Which is a word for:

a a person who writes poems?

b a long story?

c a person in a story?

d a person in a story who tells the story?

e the most important man in a story?

f a person who drinks blood?

3 Find these words in your dictionary. Use them in the sentences.

century   details   horror   method   treasure

a A good detective has to have a . . . . . to solve crimes. He must be careful and notice small . . . .

b If we find the . . . . . , we will be rich.

c These . . . . . stories were written in the last . . . . . , but they are very frightening.

After you read

4 Is Frankenstein's experiment a success?

5 How can Dantes, in *The Count of Monte Cristo*, escape from death in the sea? What is he carrying that can save his life?

6 What is unusual about Dracula and

a food?

b servants?

c mirrors?

7 Work with another student. Have this conversation.

Student A: You are Dupin. Ask the police officer what he/she saw in the house. You have also been there now. Tell the officer what happened, in your opinion.

Student B: You are a police officer. Answer Dupin's questions. Ask him for his ideas.

Stories 5–9

Before you read

8 In this part of the book there are crime stories, ghost stories and a spy story. Which do you think are more popular today? Why?

9 Find these words in your dictionary. Which is not a word for a person (alive or dead)?

ghost governess housekeeper publish representative

After you read

10 Why do you think that Mr Rochester is afraid of Mr Mason in *Jane Eyre*?

11 What is strange about Miss Hunter's job in the story of the Copper Beeches, from *A Scandal in Bohemia*?

12 Why is Dr Jekyll going to leave Mr Hyde his money in his will, in your opinion? Who is Mr Hyde?

13 Which of these sentences about *The Thirty-nine Steps* is true?

a Scudder is an old friend of Hannay.

b Scudder's enemies are foreign spies.

c Hannay doesn't think Scudder's enemies will try to kill him.

14 What do you think has happened to George in *The Man with Two Shadows*? Why?

Stories 10–14

Before you read

15 In this part of the book, there are stories about a battle, an escaped slave and a plan to put a bomb in a famous building. Which of these subjects seems most modern? Why?

16 Find these words in your dictionary. Complete the sentences.

captain Civil War politics society

The American . . . . . changed the . . . . . of the United States.

In the South, the richer people in . . . . . had to change their way of life. Before the war, the writer Mark Twain, helped the . . . . . on river boats.

After you read

17 Why are these details important in *The Return of Sherlock Holmes*?
 a the golden glasses
 b the grass near the garden path
 c Mr Smith's words before he died

18 You are Henry in *The Red Badge of Courage*. Say how you felt before the battle; when the battle started; when the enemy soldiers came towards you.

19 Why doesn't the governess in *The Turn of the Screw* realize at first that she has seen a ghost?

20 Work with another student. Have this conversation.
 Student A: You are Huck Finn's friend, Tom Sawyer. Why did Huck try to help Jim? Where were they going? Ask him.
 Student B: You are Huck. Answer Tom's questions.

21 Will Mr Verloc, in *The Secret Agent*, put a bomb in the Observatory or ask another person to do it? Why?

Writing

22 Write a police description of Dracula. Tell people not to go near him. Say why.

23 You are in trouble. Imagine what your problem is. Write a letter to Sherlock Holmes. Ask him to help you.

24 When he arrives in Scotland, Richard Hannay in *The Thirty-nine Steps* reads a story in the newspaper. It begins: *Murder in London. Man escapes dressed as a milkman*. Write the story.

25 You are the governess in *The Turn of the Screw*. Write a letter to the man who employed you. Say why you are afraid.